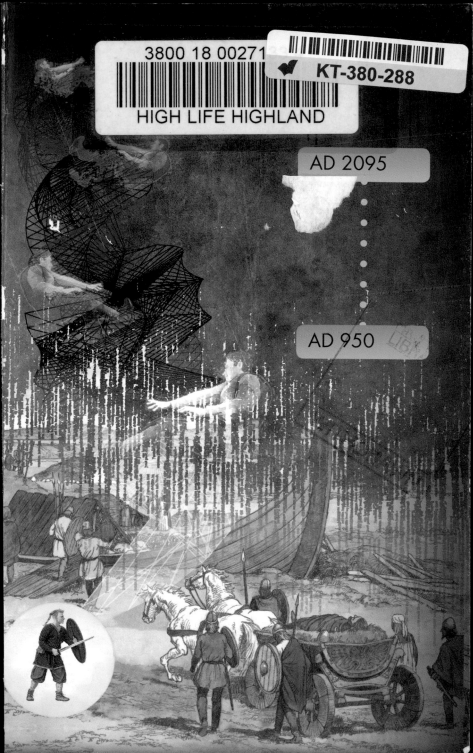

AD 2095

AD 950

First published in Great Britain by Scribo MMXVIII
Scribo, an imprint of
The Salariya Book Company
25 Marlborough Place, Brighton, BN1 1UB

ISBN 978-1-912233-05-2

Printed and bound in China.

Printed on paper from sustainable sources.

www.salariya.com

Series creator and editorial director: Jean de Brienne
Consultant: Jacqueline Morley
Illustrator: Gino D'Achille
Cover figure illustration by: Carlo Molinari
Extra illustrations by: Jennifer Skemp
Editor: Nick Pierce
Design: Mark Williams, Olivia Waller

TIMESLIP

Blood Feud

Written by
Dan Scott

Illustrated by
Gino D'Achille

SCRIBO
a SALARIYA *imprint*

CONTENTS

MISSION BRIEFING	8–9
THE VIKING WORLD	10–11
INTRODUCTION	12–15
ON THE LOOK-OUT	16–19
THE MARKET AT HEDEBY	20–25
THE HOMECOMING	24–27
TRAVELLERS' TALES	28–31
THE EMPEROR'S CITY	32–37
BLOOD FEUD	38–43
THE MEETING OF THE THING	44–47

A MESSAGE FROM ENGLAND 48–53

SEA CROSSING 54–57

VIKING YORK 58–63

THE KING'S HALL 64–69

MISSION OVER 70–71

VIKING LIFE FACTS 72–85

VISUAL ARCHIVES 86–93

GLOSSARY 94–95

INDEX 96

MISSION BRIEFING

Attention Edward Cosmo!

You have been selected for the next TIMESLIP mission:

It is your task to enter the body of a Viking boy to find out about the Vikings' experiences of settling in England.

Your name will be Egil.

Be prepared, the world you're entering is a dangerous one.

Some things you'll need to know:

The seasons in the far north can be brutal. In northern Scandinavia in midsummer the sun never sets, and in midwinter there is no daylight.

Most Vikings were pagans. They worshipped gods belonging to the pagan past of the Germanic peoples.

Vikings spoke old Norse, the language from which modern Norwegian, Swedish and Danish have developed.

The letters in the Viking alphabet are called runes. They carved these letters into wood.

The word 'Viking' means piracy or raiding. The Scandinavians had a terrifying reputation for this.

Good luck on your mission!

The TIMESLIP will commence in

3...

2...

1...

THE VIKING WORLD

Originally the Vikings lived in the areas we now call Norway, Sweden and Denmark. Many of their descendants still live in these countries today. But from the 8th to the 11th century Viking raiders, traders and settlers made their way all over Europe and beyond. They went to Russia on trading trips.

In the 9th century the Vikings made new homes in the Shetland Isles, the Orkneys, the Faroes, and Iceland, and fought to seize land in England, Ireland and France. The tough fearless settlers who went to Greenland after 986 also travelled to America, nearly five centuries before Columbus got there.

The Vikings thought that the Earth was flat, and surrounded by an ocean in which the 'world-serpent' lies coiled. In their religion, a rainbow bridge leads to Asgard, the home of the gods.

GREENLAND

ICELAND

SWEDEN

RUSSIA

NORWAY

York

ENGLAND

DENMARK

FRANCE

SPAIN

Constantinople

AFRICA

Homelands	
Settlements	
Sea routes	
Exploration and trade	
Fur	
Timber	
Pottery	
Cloth	
Weapons	
Wine	
Slaves	
Spices	
Fish	
Silk	
Fruit	
Salt	
Wheat	
Sheep	

N
W
E
S

INTRODUCTION

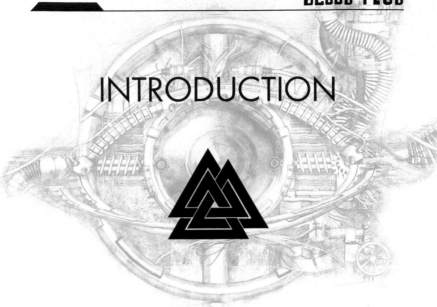

Egil is a young boy who lives near the Viking town of Hedeby in Denmark in around AD 950.

His father is a brave and wealthy merchant, who made an exciting journey across wild territory to the Swedish Viking trading post at Kiev, in modern Russia.

There, his father learned about the fabulous city of Constantinople, near the shores of the Black Sea. The Viking traders told him that in Constantinople he will be able to buy precious goods from as far away as China. He decides to visit the city and, after several adventures, returns home to his family in Denmark with a new ship laden with treasures.

While Egil's father is away from home, his capable wife and family manage his farm for him. Most Vikings were farmers and traders, like Egil's father, and not fierce and brutal warriors. They lived in comfortable wooden houses, grew a wide variety of crops, and raised animals.

The Vikings were also excellent sailors and boatbuilders. Some Viking explorers made long journeys to look for new lands to the north and west of their homeland. A few of them even reached the east coast of America.

Many more Vikings left Scandinavia to settle in the north and east of England. Some historians think that this was because there was a shortage of good farming land in Denmark.

Certainly, the Vikings settled down very successfully in their new homeland. They farmed the land and also built important trading centres such as York, where Egil's family decide to go and live.

ON THE LOOK-OUT

Whenever Egil came into the town of Hedeby, he begged the gatekeeper to let him climb up to the look-out platform above the gate. From up there, he could watch the ships sailing up the fjord from the Baltic Sea. Egil lived on a farm not far outside the town, so the gatekeeper knew him well.

'You may go up there, Egil Erikson,' he said. 'A fine Swedish boat has just come in!'

From the look-out platform you could see the whole town and the great earth bank that ran round it. Egil remembered the bank being built by order of King Harald Bluetooth. Now people could sleep in peace, without the fear of an attack from the Germans and Slavs who came on raids across the Danish border. Far away, looking westwards, you could see the merchants' ox-carts setting out on their overland trek to the great North Sea.

Egil knew that he must not stay long at the gate. He was taking a pig to market. His mother ran the family farm now as his father was away, and there was always a lot to do.

His sisters, Asa and Tove, helped with baking, weaving, brewing and butter-making. Gunnar, his brother, who was the oldest, could handle the plough and work the forge almost as well as his father, although he was not yet sixteen. The family's two thralls, or slaves, did the heavy, dirty jobs. Egil looked after the goat, the hens and the sheep.

'Still no sign of your father's ship?' asked the gatekeeper, who knew what Egil was looking for.

Each summer Egil's father went trading in the boat he shared with his cousin Thorkild. They took Frisian cloth and Rhenish wine from lands to the south of Denmark to sell to the towns along the Baltic coast. With their profits they bought amber, furs and walrus ivory, which fetched good prices at the market in Hedeby. But, last year, they had not returned.

THE MARKET AT HEDEBY

W hen he had climbed down from the look-out post, Egil continued on his way towards the centre of Hedeby.
First he walked past the site where the visiting merchants always camped. Then he came to the first houses. A girl drawing water from the well in her yard greeted him.

'Is all well at Gunnar's farm?' she asked.

'She calls it my brother's farm because

people believe that my father is dead,' thought Egil. 'But I don't believe that! Surely my father is away on a great expedition, like Grandfather before him. I have heard tell of how he went raiding in England many years ago. One day my father will return with fine goods and lots of exciting stories.'

As he neared the market, Egil had to push through the crowded streets. Country people had brought buckets of milk, casks of butter and animals to sell.

Many traders had come from lands far beyond the Danish border, for Hedeby had the biggest market in Denmark. Egil watched merchants leading the horses laden with cloth, traders selling pottery, glassware and fine Rhenish swords, and Norwegians unpacking cooking pots and lamps. Two Arabs were bargaining with a Viking slave-dealer. As Egil listened, the price was agreed and the dealer unfolded his scales to weigh the Arabs' silver. Just then Egil's pig, nosing for rubbish, gave a great tug at its leash. Egil's feet skidded on the muddy path and off went the pig, rushing towards the harbour.

Egil ran after it shouting. He had no idea that pigs could move so fast! It dashed past some women who were washing clothes on the quay, then it disappeared from sight.

He saw the Swedish boat as he raced round the corner. Its owner, to judge from the silver arm-rings he was wearing, was a very rich man. Slowly, the man turned round to face him. It was his father, home at last!

THE HOMECOMING

The pig was nowhere to be found, but that didn't matter. Egil greeted his father joyfully. He had so many questions to ask! Father explained that Cousin Thorkild was bringing their old boat back. They had bought the new Swedish boat because they had so many treasures to carry home. He ordered his men to finish unloading the boat, while he and Egil set off for the farm.

The farm, though not as big as an earl's or nobleman's, was really quite large. Its meadows provided enough hay to keep twenty cattle through the winter. The farmhouse, with a long cow byre attached, stood in the middle of a big yard. Egil ran to open the gate. The thrall who was cleaning out the byre yelled in amazement as the cart trundled in. Gunnar dropped his tools and dashed out of the forge, followed by the other thrall.

Everyone followed Father into the house. Mother, all floury from grinding the rye, leaped to her feet to meet him. Tove left her weaving.

'Call Asa,' said Mother. 'She has taken the cows to the far pasture.'

Egil ran through the bean field along the edge of the oats and the barley, calling to his sister. She could hardly believe the news and rushed back to the house in great excitement.

Father spread out gifts for everyone. There were silver drinking cups and sweet-smelling spices for the whole family to enjoy. He gave lengths of silk cloth and silver neckbands to Mother and the girls. For Gunnar, there was a sword, and to Egil he gave a silver charm and a beautiful knife. They all gasped with pleasure and thanked him. How wonderful it was to have Father home again!

'We will sacrifice an ox,' said Mother, 'and set it outside the door to thank the god Thor for Father's safe return.'

TRAVELLERS' TALES

That night they all enjoyed a happy dinner together. Mother told Father all the news about the farm; how six new calves had been born safely in the spring and that the harvest looked like being a good one.

After dinner, they sat round Father and begged him to tell his story.

'Last year we met a company of Swedish merchants who took us to a trading town they have built far along the Baltic, in the land of Finns and Slavs. The people of that land are afraid of the Swedes and they have cause

29

to be. The winters there are bitterly cold, and the Swedes live well by raiding the villages. In the spring they travel south to Kiev, a town far inland. The Swedes told us that merchants travel to Kiev from many lands. You can sell fur and slaves there for a much higher price than at Hedeby, and you can buy goods that will make your fortune at home. We decided to join them in their winter raids and see if we could take enough slaves to make the trip south worthwhile. Thor gave us luck and by spring we had plenty of slaves, fur, honey and wax. We prepared for the long journey to Kiev.

'When the snows melted we took a fleet of river boats and followed the Swedes along a wide river. We sailed upstream between huge forests where robbers lie in wait. At night we camped on the banks, but we always slept with our hands on our swords. We stopped at many of the riverside towns, but our Swedish companions said that Kiev was still many weeks ahead. The river grew narrower. We rowed until it was a trickle no wider than our boats. Then we made the slaves drag the boats overland and carry them over the roughest ground, until we reached a stream that flowed south. This bought us, at last, to the great walled town of Kiev.

'Many of the Swedes have made their homes there, and rule the Slavs. They have taken Slav wives and dress and speak like Slavs. We sold our goods and slaves without difficulty and bought silks from merchants who came from China at the eastern edge of the world, from Samarkand and from Baghdad.

THE EMPEROR'S CITY

Father continued the story of his adventures.

'In the summer the Swedish traders travel south from Kiev to the city of the Christian emperor of the east. It lies in the land of the Greeks, who call it Constantinople. We decided to go too, to sell the rest of our slaves and to see what we could buy. The Swedes travel in a great fleet for safety. The river passes through plains where savage tribes live. The river, too, is treacherous. It rushes between narrow gorges

33

in many rapids and cataracts. Sometimes we had to carry the boats along the edge of the rapids. The most terrible one is called 'The Ever-Fierce'. We had to walk six miles over land to pass it! Wild tribes were lying in wait for us, and attacked us with stones and arrows. Everyone was needed to fight them off and many good men were killed.

'Beyond the rapids there is an island with a sacred oak tree. We made sacrifices of bread and meat there to give thanks for our safe passage.

'At last the river carried us to a sea without a tide, which the local people call the Black Sea. In those lands the Sun's horse rides so close to the Earth that the light from his mane is dazzling. We followed the coast till we came to Constantinople − the emperor's city. Its palaces are made of stone and are decorated with gold. Its people know strange arts. They can lift up rivers on bridges of stone and have built a mighty temple with a round roof of stone that needs no pillars to support it.

'The Greeks like Vikings to do their fighting for them. Many Swedes serve in their army and in the emperor's bodyguard. I met one who showed me round the emperor's palace, which is full of wonders. Finally we journeyed home with profits beyond our wildest dreams.'

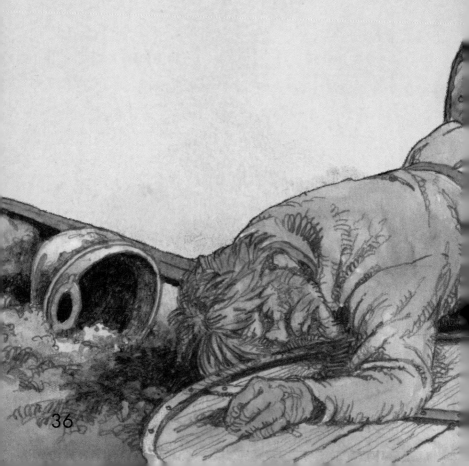

BLOOD FEUD

Egil was delighted with his new knife. No Viking freeman ever went unarmed, for he never knew when he might need to fight. News reached the farm the very next day which showed how close danger could be.

While Cousin Thorkild's family had been celebrating his homecoming, their house had been surrounded by Tostig and his men. They were members of a neighbouring family who had a long-standing feud with Thorkild's kinsmen. Tostig had threatened to set fire to the house if Thorkild did not

39

come out. To save his family, Thorkild had rushed out to face his attackers. He had wounded many before being overpowered and killed.

Egil looked at his father and brother. Surely they would avenge such a wrong.

'Tostig shall suffer for this!' said Father. 'But first we will honour Thorkild. He died with his sword in his hand! He must go with all his needs to the land beyond the grave. He shall take our new ship with him, well stocked for the journey.'

In the days that followed, many preparations were made for Thorkild's funeral. Egil went to help drag the new boat overland to the burial place.

On the day of the funeral, Thorkild's body was placed in a wooden chamber on the boat's deck. His sword, shield and spear were set beside him. His horse and hunting dogs were killed and laid in the ship.

They would live again with their master in his new life beyond the grave. He was given gold and silver arm-bands, food for the journey, cups and cooking pots. Then the ship was covered in a mound of earth. Beside the mound Thorkild's widow placed a carved stone, which recorded Thorkild's name and his heroic death. Then the family went sadly home.

43

THE MEETING OF THE THING

A t the funeral feast Father announced his decision. He would summon Tostig to appear at the meeting of the 'Thing' to answer for Thorkild's killing. He would ask the judges to impose a heavy punishment. Family honour would be satisfied and the feud would be settled.

The Thing was an assembly of all the freemen of the district. It was held several times a year to decide important matters of

trade and government. It made new laws
and judged disputes. Every man who owned
property could vote when decisions were made.

On the first day of the Thing, Father and
Gunnar, in their finest clothes, set off early for
the Thingstead, the place where the meetings
were always held. They had to make sure
that all their kinsmen were present to swear
that what they said was true. Egil followed
with a cart loaded with camping equipment.
The Thing lasted several days, so most people
brought tents and cooking utensils, and often
some goods to sell. Women did not take part,
so it was Egil's job to set up the tent and see
that meals were ready. He also had to listen
and learn, for soon he would be old enough
to vote.

The Thingstead was on Earl Svein's land.
The local earls sat on a slope with the judges
they had chosen to decide the case. First the
lawspeaker recited the law, for Viking laws
were learnt by heart, not written down. Then
Egil's father told of the feud between his
kinsmen and Tostig's family, in which Cousin
Thorkild had played no part at all. Next

Tostig spoke. It was right, he said, to avenge a great wrong by slaying the senior member of a family.

'True,' said the judges, 'but the manner of the killing was cowardly and vile. For that Tostig must be outlawed.'

'What will happen to him?' asked Egil.

'He will leave the country,' said Gunnar, 'because if we find him here we may lawfully kill him.'

A MESSAGE FROM ENGLAND

Egil rather hoped that Gunnar would seek out Tostig to avenge Thorkild's death, because he wanted to join in the attack. But soon new plans made everyone forget the hunt for Tostig. A messenger brought news from England, where Cousin Halfdan had settled. He had grown rich as a merchant in the Viking city of York. His wife was now begging Egil's father to come and live in England, since Halfdan was close to death. There was no one else to continue Halfdan's business or to protect

49

his daughter, for they had no kinsmen there.

The matter was soon settled.

'Gunnar will stay in Denmark,' said Father. 'He will marry Cousin Thorkild's daughter, and take over Thorkild's estate. Then he will have almost as much land as Earl Svein.

Egil and the women will sail with me for York, and we shall take over Halfdan's business.'

Egil wondered if Gunnar minded marrying his cousin, who was neither good-tempered nor beautiful. But Gunnar would do as his father wished, and so would she.

Gunnar was to keep the old trading boat, and so a new ship would be needed for the voyage. Egil and his father went to the boatbuilder's yard. All kinds of craft were being made; many small rowing boats, a flat-bottomed ferry boat and, almost completed, a splendid longship large enough to carry fifty armed raiders. Egil wished he could sail in a warship! Instead, he turned to look at the craftsmen at work on his family's boat. Some men were splitting oak logs into planks, while others were fastening the curved prow and stern pieces to the keel to make the backbone of the ship. They would build the hull out of tarred animal hair.

'That will go between the planks to keep the water out,' said one of the men. 'Then we'll make the inner framework, the ribs and the cross beams. Below the waterline, we'll lash it to the hull with tree roots. Nailing it all together would make the ship too rigid. She must be supple to ride the waves!'

SEA CROSSING

Egil knew how to handle a small boat, and had often been fishing along the coast. But he had never been so far from land before. They had been at sea now for three days. Yesterday they had run into a great storm. They had to lift the loose planks on the lower deck and use wooden scoops to bail out the water trapped underneath. Despite his leather cloak, Egil had been drenched. At night, in his wet clothes, he had been bitterly cold. With all the household gear and food, there was only room to put up one tent. His parents slept in that, though Father spent most of the night guiding the oar-shapped rudder that steered the boat. His sisters shared a sleeping bag made of animal skins and the thralls shared another, but Egil shivered on his own. Today the sun shone, but the waves were as high as ever.

A terrible fear seized Egil. He knew that the World Serpent wrapped itself round the edge of the world. Suppose they had sailed too far, and the sea was being lashed by its tail? Egil dared not ask his father what he thought, for a Viking must not show fear.

Instead he asked, 'Is England the last land before the edge of the world?'

'No,' said Father, 'the Norwegians have sailed far round it to the North, to a land beyond called Ireland. They have taken land there and built towns. And to the north-west, they have found an empty land they call Iceland. Whenever Vikings sail west they find new lands. Many more may lie ahead.'

'But how do we know we are sailing the right way?' asked Egil.

'By the position of the Pole Star and the Sun,' said Father. He showed Egil how the shadow of a wooden pin on a special instrument told him which way to steer. 'And look,' he said, 'that flock of birds shows that land is near. It won't be long before we reach England.'

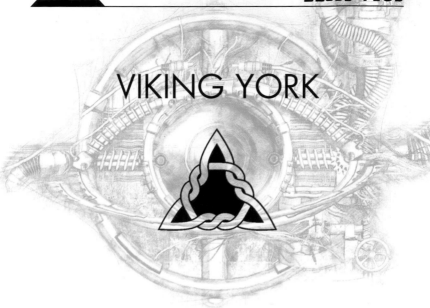

VIKING YORK

E gil felt at home in York. The buildings reminded him of Denmark. This was not surprising, for much of the town had been built by Vikings. They had taken this land, Northumbria, from the Anglo-Saxons, and now a Viking king, Erik Bloodaxe, ruled in the north and east of England. The Anglo-Saxons had taken it from the Britons long ago, and even before that the Romans, a conquering race from faraway Italy, had built a great stone city at York. Part of the Roman walls still remained.

59

61

Egil was glad to be sent out of the house to buy oysters. He enjoyed looking around the town and he decided to take the longest route back home. He turned along Cupmakers' Street to dawdle outside the workshops. He watched a woodworker turning bowls from ash and yew, and the jewellers making amber pendants and jet necklaces. The bone-carver was setting out his combs, pins and needles, and his assistant was dyeing bone buckles. Next door was a leather shop, but the hides were smelly and Egil did not linger. He caught sight of a row of decorated axe-blades on a metal-worker's stall and stopped for a closer look.

The shop's owner was striking coins out of silver disks. He placed each one between two dies and with one hammer-blow he punched a design on both sides. Thor's hammer and the name of Peter were imprinted on the coin.

'Who is Peter?' Egil asked.

The coiner was English but Egil could understand his answer well enough.

'Peter is the patron saint of York and the chief servant of Christ.'

'In Denmark we laugh at Christians,' said Egil. 'Their church bells annoy the gods.'

'We are all Christians here and no one laughs at us!' said the coiner's son, a big boy, older than Egil. 'Of course it is wise to worship the old gods as well. Even the King, Erik Bloodaxe, has become a Christian. He is a Viking and one of the greatest warlords of Odin, god of war.'

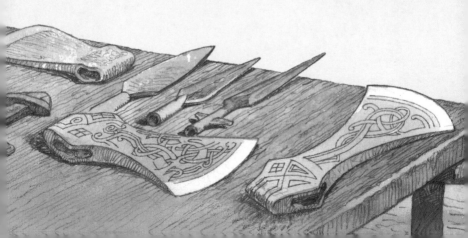

THE KING'S HALL

The coiner worked for the Master of the King's Mint. 'The Master controls the making of coins,' said the coiner's son, whose name was Alfric. 'He has placed me in the King's service. There will be a big feast today, and I have to pour wine and beer for his guests. Would you like to come to the King's Hall with me? There will be lots to see.' Egil agreed gladly. The King's Hall was larger than any house he had ever been in. A blazing fire in the centre filled the hall with light. Long tables on trestles had been set up for the feasting. Silver drinking cups were ready to be filled. Before the feast began, King Erik Bloodaxe called for a great wooden chest to be brought to him. From it he took neck-rings and arm-rings of silver and gold, and gave them to his followers to thank them for their part in his recent victory over King Eadred.

As Alfric explained to Egil, 'Eadred of the West Saxons would like to think of himself as king of all England, but we Northumbrians want a king of our own! Erik Bloodaxe and his warriors gave Eadred a good hiding. I don't think he'll be back for a while!'

Suddenly the shouting and laughter died away. The King's Skald had begun to sing about the battle. He was a good poet, and one of the king's most important servants. He went with him to the battle and watched everything that happened. Later, he composed wonderful songs to be sung on great occasions like this. People would remember his words for years to come. In this way, great men and their deeds would never be forgotten.

The Skald raised his voice and sang of the valour of Erik Bloodaxe and his men.

'Their swords shone with bright blood... Odin, god of war, will reward them in Valhalla when they enter the Hall of the Slain.'

Egil listened, spellbound. In this, his new homeland, he meant to become a great warrior like Erik Bloodaxe and his men, and to fight with the brave Northumbrians against King Eadred of Wessex. Egil could hardly wait!

MISSION OVER

Attention Edward Cosmo!

Attention Edward Cosmo!

Your mission is over. Congratulations!

Please proceed to the lab for debriefing and to share your research findings.

We will expect you in 5 minutes.

VIKING LIFE FACTS

LANDSCAPE

Vast mountains divide the Scandinavian peninsula. Sweden, on its south-east, has fertile lowlands and vast forests which are rich in iron ore. In Norway, there are mountains which drop to the sea in many places, leaving only the narrow fjords and the river valleys for farming. Denmark's flat lands are split into many islands. Iceland is a bleak place to cultivate. It is for the most part treeless, stark and barren.

HOMELAND

Vikings were not able to go shopping for everything they needed – there were no shops as we know them today. For food they had to rely on what grew well locally, and most of the things they used had to be made from what was to hand. Their homeland was of vital importance to them. In cold, harsh Greenland they had to manage very differently from the Danish Vikings who were much further south.

THE WILD-LIFE

Summertime is short, and the winters are long and cold, though they may have been slightly milder in Viking times. The wildlife in the Viking homelands were well adapted to these conditions, and were useful to people in a number of ways. The bear, the fox and the marten supplied them with warm coats and coverings, and the deer and the elk provided meat. Furs and hides also provided valuable goods to sell.

THE PLANTS & TREES

Vikings often lived near large areas of forest, especially in Norway and Sweden. If there was not enough farmland to support everyone, they may well have had to cut down trees to create enough land to grow food. Trees were valuable, providing fuel for heating, cooking and metal-working, and timber to build houses and boats. If people could not spare land to grow vegetables they had to forage for wild plants.

THE SEASONS

The Vikings often found themselves living very far north indeed. Because of the tilt of the globe, the regions near the poles have extreme variations in the length of night and day. In summertime the Vikings would have had a very long working day, while in winter they would spend many weeks indoors, in almost total darkness.

HUNTING & FISHING

Those living in the more northerly Viking lands had to rely heavily on hunting and trapping to increase their food supply. The sea was teeming with many different kinds of fish; there were also whales and seals to be speared, and sea birds to be shot or snared and their eggs gathered. The rivers were full of salmon. In Scandinavia Vikings were able to hunt wild boar, red deer and, in the far north, reindeer.

VIKING LIFESTYLE

The word 'Viking' means piracy, or raiding. The Scandinavians' reputation for raiding terrified their Christian and Slav neighbours. However, many Vikings led peaceful, stay-at-home lives. If a person survived birth, they could expect on average to live for about fifty years. Most Vikings were free, but some were born as slaves, to slave parents.

FARMING

In Denmark and southern Sweden, Viking farms might have been in a village. Farmers would have been able to grow wheat and barley, provided that the land was level and open. They also kept domestic animals such as pigs and cattle. In the far north, only grass grew well so the northern Vikings relied on their animals. There the Vikings led an isolated life, for large areas of pasture were needed to support the animals of just one family.

WRITING

Viking letters were called runes. The Vikings did not use pens. They carved letters into wood. Runes were formed of straight strokes, as wood grain made curves harder to cut. Inscriptions in memory of people were cut on large stones.

THE LANGUAGE

The Vikings spoke what scholars today call Old Norse, the language from which modern Norwegian, Swedish and Danish developed. It varied little throughout Scandinavia. Vikings who left their homeland were able to talk to 'foreign' Vikings quite easily. Modern English speakers would easily recognise some words: egg, skill, sky and anger are just a few words the English learned from their Viking invaders.

VIKING NAMES

Many Viking names are still in use now – Thora, Ingrid, Astrid, Olaf, Eric and Harald, for instance. The Vikings were very fond of nicknames: Harald Bluetooth, Ivar the Boneless, Radnor Lothbrok (hairy trousers), Thord the Short (he was very tall!)

VIKING BELIEFS

Until quite late in the Viking period (which lasted from the 9th century when Vikings began raiding, to the 11th, when they settled down) most Vikings were pagans. They worshipped gods belonging to the pagan past of the Germanic peoples. Some did convert to Christianity, yet they still worshipped their pagan gods. Viking values may seem strange to us – they led hard lives and had no pity for weak people.

TIMELINE

At the dawn of the Viking age there were three great powers in the western world: the Franks who ruled what is now France and Germany, the Byzantines, who had inherited the eastern half of the Roman empire, and the Arabs, whose civilisation extended from western Asia, through North Africa to Spain. Most of Europe, including Britain and Ireland, was Christian by this time, though the Scandinavians and the Slavs of eastern Europe were still pagan.

The Scandinavians were already prosperous traders in the areas around the Baltic Sea. Before AD 700 the Swedes had expanded eastwards, setting up colonies along the Baltic coast. At the end of the 8th century the Norwegians made the first of what were to be repeated Viking attacks on countries to the west. A combination of greed for riches, and the need to find new land probably led to these attacks.

AD 793 Norwegian Vikings attack and destroy the monastery on the island of Lindisfarne, which is off the Northumbrian coast of England. England at this time is divided into several small kingdoms of which Mercia, Wessex, East Anglia and Northumbria are the most important. There is no royal authority that is strong enough to organise a successful defence against these attacks.

AD 795 Norwegian Vikings attack St Columba's monastery at Iona in western Scotland, and raid the coast of Wales.

AD 800 Norwegian Vikings land in the Orkney and Shetland Isles, and the Faroes. These provide a base for raids on Ireland.

AD 828 Irish chroniclers record that their country is overrun by Viking pirates.

AD 834 Danes attack and raid the Frisian trading centre at Dorestad on the Rhine, and begin to launch regular attacks on the lands of the Franks.

AD 835 The Danes attack Sheppey, an island at the mouth of the Thames, in England.

AD 841 Norwegian Vikings begin to settle permanently in Ireland. Dublin is founded. Ireland serves as a starting-point for the colonisation of the Isle of Man, south-western Scotland, and north-western England. In the same year the Danes sail up the River Seine in France and attack and raid Rouen.

AD 843 The Danes sail up the River Loire in France and attack Nantes. They destroy towns and monasteries all over western France. The terrified peasants flee, and the land is laid waste.

AD 844 Vikings capture Seville in Spain, but only manage to hold it for a week as the Arabs soon put them to flight.

AD 845 Vikings attacks and plunder Paris in France, and Hamburg in Germany. Charles the Bald, who is king of the West Franks, pays the first of many large payments, known as Danegeld. This was used by rulers to try to buy off the Vikings and stop their attacks.

AD 850 Danes begin to overwinter in England.

AD 859 A fleet of ships enters the Mediterranean Sea, where the Vikings raid for three years. They attack Spain, southern France, North Africa and Italy.

AD 860–874 The first Viking settlers arrive in Iceland.

AD 865 A large Viking force lands in England seeking land to settle.

AD 866 It captures York. By the early 870s Vikings control most of eastern England. They begin to share out the land. A further expansion is defeated by Alfred, King of Wessex, who makes its leaders accept Christianity.

AD 886 A treaty between Alfred and Guthrum defines the frontier of the Danelaw. Alfred's successors gradually regain control in England though the Viking settlers remain.

AD 891 Vikings are defeated by the Franks. The Viking threat grows weaker in Europe.

AD 911 Throughout the 10th century Swedish Vikings are active along trade routes in Russia.

AD 960 Harald Bluetooth, King of Denmark, converts his country to Christianity.

AD 980 A new wave of Viking attacks and raids on England begins.

AD 986 Eric the Red goes to Greenland.

AD 991 The English make the first in a series of Danegeld payments.

AD 992 Leif Ericsson leaves Greenland to look for land to the west.

AD 994 A fleet of 94 ships, led by Olaf Tryggvason of Norway and Svein Forkbeard of Denmark, attacks London.

AD 995 Olaf, the Christian King of Norway, makes his people convert.

AD 1009 Chief Thorkel the Tall ravages England for three years and extorts 48,000 pounds of silver.

AD 1013 Svein returns, and by 1017 controls all of England. His son Cnut rules until 1035. Cnut gains control of Norway and Sweden, and is also ruler of Denmark.

AD 1042 The accession of an English king, Edward the Confessor, ends Danish rule in England.

AD 1066 The Norwegian king Harald Hardraada invades England and is killed in battle at Stamford Bridge, near York. He is the last great Viking ruler.

AD 1100 Close of the Viking age as Viking settlers become absorbed into the local populations.

VISUAL ARCHIVES

Vikings living in different parts of Scandinavia formed three distinct groups: the Danes, the Swedes and the Norwegians. Each group set off in a different direction for its voyages of plunder, trade or exploration.

Our best sources of information about the everyday lives of the Vikings are the many archaeological remains that survive from the Viking period. Coins, weapons, jewellery, cooking pots, and remains of ships all help archaeologists to build up a picture of life in Viking times.

Vikings made many beautiful objects out of metal, as well as dangerous weapons of war. They forged locally produced iron to make heavy farm equipment, and traded for jewels and precious metals with merchants from distant lands, or seized them as plunder.

VISUAL ARCHIVES

Viking women span and wove wool into thread. Women often took responsibility for running the farm while fathers or husbands were away.

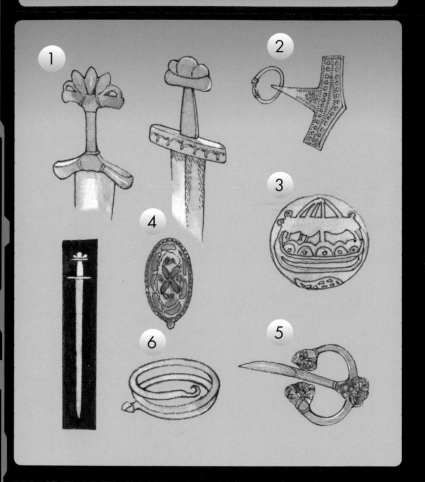

VISUAL ARCHIVES

The Vikings also loved jewellery and display, and many examples of their workmanship can still be seen today.

1 Sword handles
2 Silver pendant
3 Silver coin
4 Bronze brooch
5 Cloak fastener
6 Silver bracelet

Runes, the Viking letters, were carved into wood.

VISUAL ARCHIVES

1 Comb
2 Ploughshare
3 Heads of battle axes
4 Buckle
5 Wooden utensils

6 Soapstone bowl
7 Iron cauldron
8 Kitchen pots
9 Wooden utensil

Viking houses were built of wood, with a turf or thatch roof.

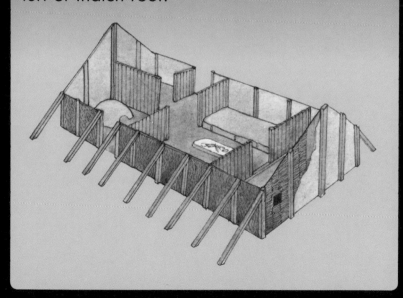

VISUAL ARCHIVES

Vikings were excellent sailors and boat builders. Most Viking ships were cargo boats, not warships.

ship's weather vane

compass

Cutaway of a cargo ship

GLOSSARY

Baltic relating to the area around the Baltic Sea, a sea in the Atlantic Ocean enclosed by the Scandinavian countries.

Byre a cowshed.

Cataracts large waterfalls.

Erik Bloodaxe a Viking ruler who was briefly king of Norway and king of Northumbria in England.

Fjord a deep inlet of the sea that extends far inland between high cliffs.

Frisian of the Germanic tribe who lived around the coastal regions of the Netherlands and north-western Germany.

Hull the bottom, sides and deck of a ship, but often used to refer to the bottom only.

Keel the structure extending along the length of the bottom of a boat that supports the framework of the whole. In Viking times, it was always made from wood.

Kiev the capital city of modern-day Ukraine and one of the oldest cities in eastern Europe.

Pole Star A bright star that remains fixed in position above the North Pole throughout the night and therefore can be used by sailors to navigate.

Prow the front part of a ship.

Rhenish of the culture and peoples living in the region of the River Rhine in central and western Europe.

Rudder a structure extending vertically into the water from the stern of a boat, used to steer the vessel.

Scandinavian relating to Scandinavia, a region of northern Europe centred around the modern-day countries of Denmark, Norway and Sweden, occupied by Germanic peoples with a similar culture and languages.

Skald A Viking poet

Stern the rear part of a ship.

World Serpent a gigantic serpent in Norse mythology wrapped around the world with its tail in its mouth. The Vikings believed that if the serpent ever let go of its tail, the world would end.

York a walled city in north Yorkshire in England, founded by the Romans and subsequently occupied by the Vikings.

INDEX

America 10, 14
Asgard 10

Bloodaxe, Erik 59, 63, 66, 67, 94

Christianity 33, 63, 75, 78–79, 83–84
Constantinople 11, 13, 33, 35

Danegeld 82, 84
Denmark 10, 11, 13–15, 19, 22, 50, 59, 63, 72, 76, 84, 95

Ericsson, Leif 84

farming 14–15, 18, 25–26, 29, 72, 74, 76, 86–87
funeral rites 40–41, 45

Greenland 10–11, 73, 84

Iceland 10–11, 56, 72, 82

Norway 10, 72, 74, 84, 85, 86, 94, 95

paganism 9, 78–79
piracy 9, 75, 80

runes 9, 76, 89

sacrifice 27, 35
Sweden 10–11, 72, 74, 76, 85, 95

Thing, the 45–47
Thor 27, 30, 62

Valhalla 67

World Serpent 10, 56, 95

York 15, 49, 51, 59, 62, 83, 85, 95